# READ WELL

# All About Dinosaurs

## UNITS 10, 11

ISBN 978-1-60218-553-1
ISBN 1-60218-553-0
167273

12  11  10  09          3  4  5  6

Sopris West®
EDUCATIONAL SERVICES

A Cambium Learning® Company

BOSTON, MA · LONGMONT, CO

# UNIT 11 • Dog Detective

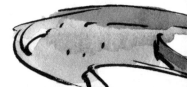

5

## UNIT 10
# Dino Discoveries

# Going on a Dino Dig

by *Marilyn Sprick*
*illustrated by Jana Christy*

Look at the picture. The Wrights are packing up. How do you think the family feels?

## Chapters 1, 2

# Vocabulary

★ **def·i·nite·ly**

**Definitely** means for sure.

If you drop an egg, it will *definitely* make a mess.

Use the word *definitely* and answer this question: Would you like to go to Disneyland?

★ **ex·pe·di·tion**

An **expedition** is a special journey to study or discover something.

The astronauts went on an *expedition* to the moon. If you could go on an expedition, where would you go?

**★ = New**

## ★ wear·y

**Weary** means very tired.

Sally was *weary* from her long hike. How did she feel?

## ★ lo·cate

**Locate** means to find where something is.

We used the map to *locate* the treasure. What else could you locate with a map?

## ★ or·gan·ize

**Organize** means to arrange or plan things.

Louisa arranged the fruit on the table. What did Louisa do?

## ★ de·ter·mined

When you try very hard and do not give up, you are **determined**.

Stan was *determined* to win the race.

If you are determined to finish your work on time, what should you do?

## Chapter 1

# The E-Mail

Think about the chapter title. What do you think will happen in this chapter?

The old SUV rumbled down the highway. Benjamin Franklin Thomas Edison Wright, his brother, Albert Einstein Louis Braille Wright, and his father, Dr. Wilbur Wright, were excited to be on their way.

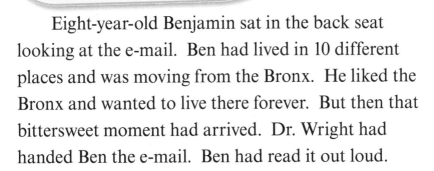

We're going on a dino dig.
A dino dig, a dino dig!
We're going to find big bones.
We're going to find big bones.
Are we there yet?
Are we there yet?
Not yet!
Not yet!

Eight-year-old Benjamin sat in the back seat looking at the e-mail. Ben had lived in 10 different places and was moving from the Bronx. He liked the Bronx and wanted to live there forever. But then that bittersweet moment had arrived. Dr. Wright had handed Ben the e-mail. Ben had read it out loud.

---

Tuesday, June 1  2:14 PM

**Subject:** Dino Dig
**From:** Ralph Knight
**Date:** June 1
**To:** Dr. Wilbur Wright

Dear Wilbur:

We have funding for our dinosaur expedition.

The bones that were found are definitely dinosaur bones.

Can you come? We have a job for you.

Ralph Knight

P.S. After the expedition, we would need you to stay and work with us at the lab.

---

Who is the story about? What do you know about Ben, Albert, and their dad? Why was reading the e-mail a *bittersweet* moment?

Albert had started jumping up and down.

Without thinking, Ben had hooted, "A dino dig! Dad, we have to go. Dino bones! Wow! It could be a T. rex or maybe even a velociraptor."

Soon the Wrights were packed and ready to move again. Traffic out of New York was terrible. It seemed like everyone was leaving the city for summer vacation.

How can you tell Albert is excited to go on a dinosaur *expedition*? How can you tell Ben is excited to go on a dinosaur expedition?

Four days later, a weary Dr. Wright and his boys walked into the campsite singing:

We're going on a dino dig.
A dino dig, a dino dig!
We're going to find big bones.
We're going to find big bones.
Are we there yet?
Are we there yet?
Miles and miles later,
Miles and miles later,
Yes, we are there!
Yes, we are there!

A half-dozen worried adults were at the campsite, sipping coffee and talking. A tall thin man walked over to greet the three Wrights. He tipped his dusty hat and stuck out his hand. Dr. Wright shook the man's hand and said, "Good to see you, Ralph."

Why was Dr. Wright *weary*? Who is Ralph?

Without hesitating, Ralph said, "Good to see you, Wilbur. You're just in time. We have a problem."

**Think and Talk**

MAIN CHARACTERS

1. Who is the story about?

INFERENCE

2. How did Ben and Albert feel about moving again? Why?

INFERENCE

3. What do you think the problem is at the dino dig?

PERSONAL RESPONSE

4. If someone asked you to go on a dino dig, what would you say? Why?

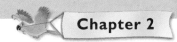

## Chapter 2

# Albert Goes Missing

At dawn the next day, people were already moving about. Hammers, chisels, and brushes sat in crates. Ralph handed Dr. Wright a small computer. It was being used to locate the dinosaur bones.

Ralph said, "We've come all this way and have found nothing. According to the computer, we are standing right where the dinosaur bones should be. I don't understand why we can't find the bones. They are missing." Dr. Wright began to work with the computer.

What is Ralph's problem? What is Dr. Wright trying to do with the computer?

Eggs, toast, and ham slices were sitting out for everyone to grab. Stomach rumbling, Ben decided to get some breakfast. He crawled into the little pup tent to get Albert, but Albert's sleeping bag was empty.

Ben wandered around the small camp looking for Albert. Finally, Ben went to find his father. "Dad," said Ben. "Albert's gone. He must have wandered off."

Ralph organized a rescue party. Everyone was determined to find little Albert. Still, Dr. Wright looked worried.

Everyone went in different directions hollering, "Albert! Albert!" Ben and Dr. Wright went east.

An hour later, they stopped to rest. Dr. Wright leaned over the mountain stream and splashed cold water on his hot, worried face.

Suddenly, Ben said, "Dad, listen. Do you hear that?"

It was hard to hear anything but the rushing of the mountain stream. Ben yelled, "Albert!"

What is the problem? Why is Dr. Wright hot and worried?

Then Ben and Dr. Wright whooped. They could hear Albert calling, "Dad, Ben . . ."

Dr. Wright and Ben scrambled over to a huge fallen tree. They could barely see Albert's head. He stood in a small space between two huge logs. He was just too small to get out by himself.

Why hadn't Albert returned to the camp?

Albert's eyes kind of puddled up. As Dr. Wright reached down to pull him out, he said, "It's okay, Albert. We've got you now."

Albert hugged Dr. Wright's leg. Then he looked up and asked, "Did you see 'em?"

"See what?" asked Dr. Wright.

"The footprints," said Albert. "There were footprints. I followed them, and then I didn't know where I was."

Dr. Wright smiled. "It's okay, Albert."

Albert said, "I really mean it! Just like that boy in Canada. I found dinosaur footprints."

Was Dr. Wright angry with Albert? Why or why not? What does Albert think he found?

**Chapter 3**

# Vocabulary

### hes·i·tate

**Hesitate** means to stop before saying or doing something. You hesitate because you aren't sure what to do.

The water in the pool was very cold, so I *hesitated* before jumping in. I wasn't sure I wanted to jump in the pool, so I . . .

### ★ in·sist

**Insist** means to communicate very strongly what you want or how you feel.

It was late, so Mom *insisted* that I go to bed.

What's another way to say "Mom told me that I'd better clean my room"?

### ★ crouch

**Crouch** means to squat down close to the ground.

Andrew *crouched* down so he could crawl under his desk. Who would like to show us how to crouch?

★ = New

## Idioms and Expressions

### ★ save the day

**Save the day** means to keep something from going wrong.

We thought we were lost, but Mike had a map and *saved the day*.

We forgot our bat and ball for the big game. What could someone do to save the day?

**Now You Try It!**
Try defining the next word. Then look up the word in the glossary. Your definition might be better!

### ex·pe·di·tion

Start with "An *expedition* is . . ."
Let's find the word on page 89.

★ = New

## Chapter 3

# Chip, Chip, Dig, Dig

Who is the story about? What are they doing? At the end of Chapter 2,
what did Albert say he had found?

Everyone was happy to hear that Albert was safe. The expedition team gathered back at camp. With Albert found, Ralph was once again determined to find the dinosaur bones.

Dr. Wright said, "Albert, go tell Ralph what you found." Albert hesitated. Then he went and pulled on Ralph's pant leg.

Albert said, "Come see."

Ralph said, "Not now."

Albert looked at Ben and Dr. Wright. They both nodded and smiled.

Albert said, "Come see."

Ralph said, "Albert, I'm busy."

Albert stood his ground. He insisted, "Come see."

Why did Albert *hesitate* when his dad told him to talk with Ralph? Why did Albert *insist* that Ralph come with him?

Finally, Ralph took Albert's hand and went with him.

Ben whispered to Dr. Wright, "What do you think Ralph will say?"

Ben and Dr. Wright watched as Ralph crouched down and crawled on all fours under the roots of the big tree. For a moment, it was quiet. Then they heard a yee haw!

Ben and Dr. Wright just grinned. Ben said, "I think Albert has saved the day."

Dr. Wright said, "Kind of looks that way."

Look at the picture. Describe what is happening. What do you think will happen next?

| BEN'S FIELD LOG | |
|---|---|
| Tuesday, June 15 | —Albert leads team to prints under fallen tree.<br>—Team clears fallen trees from riverbank.<br>    a. 123 prints uncovered<br>    b. 28 prints belong to carnivores (theropods, T. rex?)<br>    c. 95 prints belong to herbivores (ornithopods)<br>—Ralph thinks T. rex may have been hunting the ornithopods.<br>—Perfect or what? |

**Think and Talk**

INFERENCE

**1.** How did Albert save the day?

SUMMARIZATION

**2.** What did you learn from Ben's field log?

# A Dinosaur Timeline

*by Ann Watanabe
and Marilyn Sprick
illustrated by Stephen Aitken*

**K-W-L**
**(modified)**

### Dinosaurs

| What do we think we know? | What do we want to know? | What did we learn? |
| --- | --- | --- |
|  |  |  |

Look at the picture. What does it show? Where do you think this dinosaur is?

## Chapters 1, 2

# Vocabulary

### i·ma·gine

**Imagine** means to make a picture of something in your mind. You can also imagine how something might smell, taste, and feel.

*Imagine* life without cars. How would you get from place to place?

### ★ ex·tinct

**Extinct** means died out. Animals and plants that are extinct are no longer found on Earth.

Are there any dinosaurs on Earth today? Why not?

### ★ roam

**Roam** means to wander or walk around freely.

What's another way to say "Dinosaurs walked around Earth for millions of years"?

★ = New

## ★ fas·ci·nate

**Fascinate** means to hold someone's interest. Things that fascinate us are very interesting.

Insects *fascinate* Ann, so she wants to study them. What's something you would like to study? Use the word *fascinate* to explain why.

## ★ re·mains

**Remains** are what is left of something.

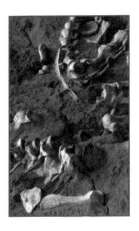

Dinosaurs left behind bones, teeth, eggs, and tracks. All of these things are . . .

## ★ fos·sil

A **fossil** is the remains of a plant or animal that lived long ago. A fossil is made of rock or found in rock.

Touch the picture. What does it show?

## ★ re·al·ize

**Realize** means to suddenly understand something.

Tom *realized* that he was late for dinner. When Tom realized he was late, he . . .

**Now You Try It!**
Try defining the next word. Then look up the word in the glossary. Your definition might be better!

### vast

Start with "*Vast* is another word for . . ."
Let's find the word on page 92.

**Chapter 1**

# 165 Million Years Ago

Millions of years ago, enormous dinosaurs ruled the Earth. Argentinosaurus (Are-jen-teen-o-sore-us) may have stood as tall as a six-story building and weighed as much as 20 elephants. Imagine that! It was the time of the dinosaurs.

Close your eyes. *Imagine* 20 elephants. One Argentinosaurus weighed as much as 20 elephants. If I said Argentinosaurus was big, would the word *big* describe it? What would be a better word?

### Dinosaurs Lived Long Ago

No human being has ever seen a live dinosaur. They became extinct long before people were on Earth. We know dinosaurs lived on Earth because they left behind their eggs, their footprints, and their huge bones.

Dinosaurs lived on Earth for more than 165 million years. Then about 65 million years ago, they disappeared.

What will you learn in this section? Has any person ever seen a living dinosaur? Why not? How do we know about dinosaurs?

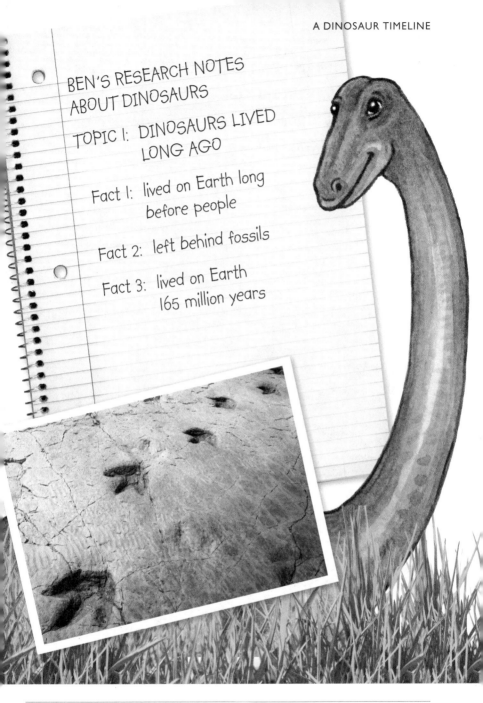

BEN'S RESEARCH NOTES
ABOUT DINOSAURS

TOPIC I:  DINOSAURS LIVED
         LONG AGO

Fact I:  lived on Earth long
         before people

Fact 2:  left behind fossils

Fact 3:  lived on Earth
         165 million years

Where do you think Ben found the facts for his notes?  What facts did he
write down?  What question does Ben's research notes answer?

A timeline helps us understand when things happened. Look at the timeline below. It shows when the first dinosaurs appeared and when they died out. Can you find when people first appeared on Earth?

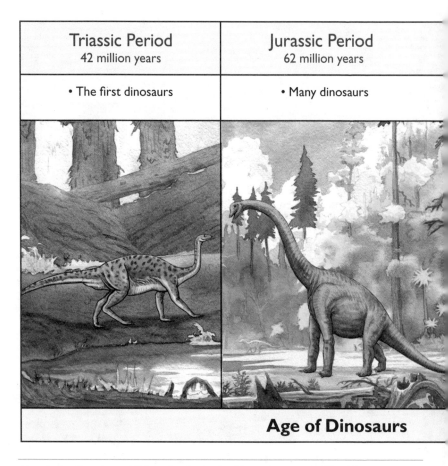

| Triassic Period | Jurassic Period |
| :---: | :---: |
| 42 million years | 62 million years |
| • The first dinosaurs | • Many dinosaurs |

**Age of Dinosaurs**

Touch the first box. This tells about the Triassic period. The Triassic period lasted 42 million years. Read the words next to the dot. What happened in the Triassic period?

Touch the next box. This is the Jurassic period. What does the timeline tell you about dinosaurs in that time?

## Quaternary Period
### 1.8 million years

• The first people

| Cretaceous Period | Tertiary Period |
|---|---|
| 79 million years | 63.2 million years |
| • Largest number of dinosaurs and many different dinosaurs | • No dinosaurs |

**Age of Mammals**

Touch the third box. This box shows the Cretaceous period. The Cretaceous period lasted 79 million years. What do we know about dinosaurs in that period?

Touch the next box. This shows the Tertiary period. What does the timeline tell you about dinosaurs in that period? What do you think happened to dinosaurs?

### Earth When Dinosaurs Lived

When dinosaurs first roamed Earth, it was a very different place than we know today. Scientists call the land where the first dinosaurs lived Pangaea (Pan-jee-uh).

Pangaea was a super continent—one vast continent. There were no oceans to cross, so dinosaurs walked freely everywhere.

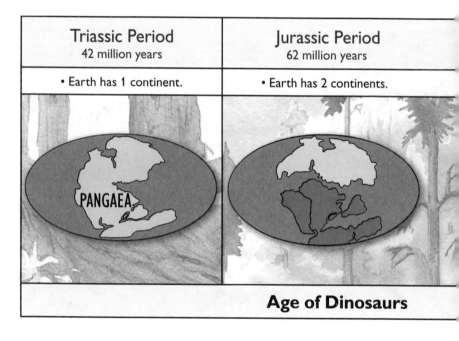

| Triassic Period<br>42 million years | Jurassic Period<br>62 million years |
|---|---|
| • Earth has 1 continent. | • Earth has 2 continents. |

**Age of Dinosaurs**

---

Touch Pangaea. This shows Earth 42 million years ago. Why were the dinosaurs able to walk wherever they wanted to go? Dinosaurs lived in the Triassic period, the Jurassic period, and the Cretaceous period. Touch the three boxes that show when dinosaurs lived.

Dinosaurs left their tracks where they lived, and they left their bones where they died. Dinosaurs lived in every part of the world, including Antarctica.

Then Pangaea began to break and slowly drift apart. By the Cretaceous period, there were seven continents.

| Quaternary Period |
| --- |
| 1.8 million years |

| Cretaceous Period | Tertiary Period |
| --- | --- |
| 79 million years | 63.2 million years |
| • Earth has 7 continents. | |
| | |
| | **Age of Mammals** |

Touch what Earth looks like now. Why can't animals walk wherever they want? Now touch the space that shows the Quaternary period. That shows how long people have lived on Earth.

**Think and Talk**

FACT

**1.** How long were dinosaurs on Earth?

DRAWING CONCLUSIONS

**2.** Why can't you see a living dinosaur now?

ASKING QUESTIONS

**3.** What would you like to learn about dinosaurs?

 **Chapter 2**

# Discovering Dinosaurs

What are we going to learn about in this section?

## How We Know About Dinosaurs

Dinosaurs have always fascinated people. We find and study their bones, and then we make guesses about what they looked like and how they lived. Sometimes we find that our best guesses about these animals are wrong.

Look at the picture. What guesses can you make about how this dinosaur lived by looking at its skeleton?

When dinosaurs died, their bones, teeth, and tracks were covered with sand and mud. Over time, dinosaur remains turned into fossils.

Look at the picture. If you were on this dino dig, what would you be thinking?

## Fossils

TOPIC 2: FOSSILS
Fact 1:

What are we going to learn about in this section? I'll write the topic in our research notes. As we read, listen for facts that explain how fossils are formed.

How is it possible to find the remains of dinosaurs millions of years after they died out? This is what happened.

Like other animals, dinosaurs lived, laid eggs, raised babies, and then died. If a dinosaur died near a stream, the sand and mud from the stream covered up the body. Over time, the dinosaur remains turned into stone and became fossils. Today, we find dinosaur fossils all over the world.

TOPIC 2: FOSSILS
Fact 1: Dino died
Fact 2:
Fact 3:

Find two or three facts that I can write in our notes that explain how *fossils* are formed. Look in your book for what happens first. What happens next?

## Finding Fossils Long Ago

TOPIC 3: FINDING FOSSILS

What are we going to learn about in this section? What's the next topic to write on our research notes?

Listen for two or three facts that tell what people thought about dinosaurs long ago.

For thousands of years, people have been finding dinosaur fossils. One of the first dinosaur fossils was found in China more than 3,500 years ago. Imagine finding a large, strange-looking tooth. The people in China didn't know about dinosaurs, so they thought they had discovered the tooth of a dragon!

**China: 3,500 years ago**     **England: 400 years ago**

Was it a dragon's tooth?     Was it a giant's thighbone?

About 400 years ago in England, people found an enormous thighbone. The people of England didn't know about dinosaurs either. They thought they had found the bone of a giant!

During the next few hundred years, more and more bones were discovered. Finally, about 150 years ago, people realized the bones were from animals they had never seen. The animals were given the name dinosaur, which means terrible lizard.

TOPIC 3: FINDING FOSSILS

Fact 1: China, 3500 years Dragon's Tooth

What facts can we write in our notes? What did people think about dinosaurs 3,500 years ago, 400 years ago, and 150 years ago?

**FACT**

1. What did dinosaurs leave behind?

**EXPLANATION**

2. How is a fossil formed?

**EXPLANATION**

3. What did people long ago think about the dinosaur fossils they found?

**ASKING QUESTIONS**

4. What else would you like to learn about dinosaurs?

**Chapter 3**

# Vocabulary

## ★ ob·sessed

To be **obsessed** with something means to think about that thing all the time.

The dog was *obsessed* with its bone. What did the dog think about all the time?

## ★ boast

**Boast** means to brag. When someone boasts, he or she talks proudly about something.

Courtney *boasted* about winning first place. Have you ever boasted about something?

## ★ bick·er

**Bicker** means to argue about things that are not important.

Sammy and Will argued about who should be first in line. What did they do? Use your vocabulary word.

**Now You Try It!**

Try defining each word. Then look up the word in the glossary. Your definition might be better!

### di·no·saur

Start with "A *dinosaur* is . . ."
Let's find the word on page 89.

### cu·ri·ous

Start with "Someone who is *curious* . . ."
Let's find the word on page 88.

 **★ = New**

**Chapter 3**

# Hunting for Dinosaurs in the United States

What do you think you will learn about in this section?

About 150 years ago, people found dinosaur bones in the United States. A nearly complete dinosaur skeleton was dug up in New Jersey. Scientists named the dinosaur Hadrosaurus (Had-roh-sore-us). Can you imagine the excitement? People discovered that Hadrosaurus walked on two legs. Up to this time, people thought all dinosaurs walked on four legs.

What was important about finding Hadrosaurus? How do you think people learned that Hadrosaurus walked on two legs?

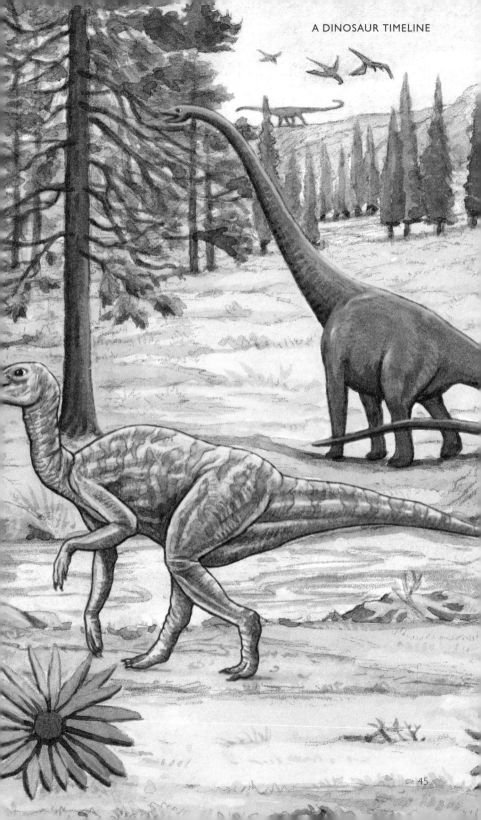

## The Bone Wars

What are you going to learn about in this section? What do you think the Bone Wars were about?

By the 1870s, people were very curious about dinosaurs. Charles Marsh and Edward Cope became so obsessed with fossil hunting that they started what we now call the Bone Wars.

Marsh and Cope each wanted to be the best dinosaur hunter. The men boasted about their finds. They bickered. They spied on each other, and they even stole bones from one another. For 30 years, the Bone Wars continued.

Charles Marsh

Edward Cope

What were Marsh and Cope *obsessed* about? What did each man want?

Marsh and Cope were each determined to be the first to discover new kinds of dinosaurs. The two men discovered 142 new kinds of dinosaurs!

Sadly, Marsh and Cope were in such a rush to find new kinds of dinosaur bones that they were not very careful. They destroyed many bones by using dynamite to blast away rock.

BEN'S RESEARCH NOTES
ABOUT DINOSAURS

TOPIC 4: The Bone Wars

Fact 1:   Marsh and Cope obsessed with
          dinosaur fossils

Fact 2:   Each wanted to be the first
          to discover new dinosaurs.

Fact 3:   Started Bone Wars

Fact 4:   Discovered 142 new kinds
          of dinosaurs

What was good about the Bone Wars? What was bad about the Bone Wars? Are there any facts you would add to Ben's notes to explain what the Bone Wars were?

## A Dinosaur Dig Today

What will we learn in this section?

Now when people go on a dinosaur dig, they are very careful. They are careful not to break any of the bones. Dinosaur hunters dig out big blocks of stone, leaving the fossils untouched by shovels and picks. They put special glue on the bones and even put a coat of plaster on them. Then the fossils are carefully shipped back to a lab.

In the lab, workers carefully cut off the plaster and then use tiny picks to free the fossils from the rock. Finally, they use paintbrushes to brush off the dust.

What facts tell you that people today are very careful when they dig up dinosaur fossils? Look at the picture above. What is the man in the lab doing?

Once the bones have been carefully chipped out of the rock, scientists can study the fossils. They ask many questions. They use computers. They rebuild the dinosaur with as many real bones as possible. Using the facts they know and the facts they learn, scientists keep finding out more about these fascinating creatures.

Today, there are many places you can go to see dinosaur skeletons. People can even go on a dinosaur dig.

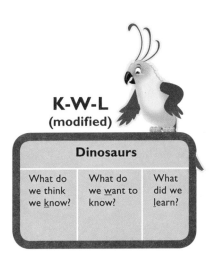

**K-W-L**
(modified)

| Dinosaurs | | |
| --- | --- | --- |
| What do we think we know? | What do we want to know? | What did we learn? |

How could you find out more about dinosaurs?

**PERSONAL RESPONSE**

1. Would you like to go on a dinosaur dig? Why or why not?

**GENERATING IDEAS**

2. If you found a new type of dinosaur, you might get to name it. What would you name your dinosaur?

# Fluency

## There's A Dinosaur in My Bed

*by Paula Rich*

*illustrated by Janet Pederson*

The day began like any plain ordinary day.    8
I woke up and made my bed. (I always make    18
my bed.) I walked to school and sat at my same    29
old desk. I had a plain ordinary peanut butter    38
sandwich for lunch. I walked home. Like I said,    47
it was a plain ordinary day until I opened the    57
door to my room.    61

Two enormous blue eyes peeked out from    68
under my blanket. "Who are you?" I cried.    76
"Why are you in my nice tidy bed?"    84

"My name is Sue. How do you do?" said    93
the creature.    95

"There's a dinosaur in my bed!" I    102
exclaimed. "This is quite strange! It's only half    110
past four. It's not bedtime yet. What are you    119
doing? Why are you here?"    124

---

The day began as an ordinary day. What changed it?

# Fluency

Sue yawned. "I've been in a museum, but 8
life was boring. I'd much rather be out in the 18
world exploring! 20

"So one night I just walked out the door. 29
No more plain ordinary days for this dinosaur. 37
I roamed through forests and mountains, cities 44
and towns. What fun! But finally I began to 53
slow down. 55

"I came to your house and found your cozy 64
soft bed. A nice quiet place to call home, I said! 75
So that's why I'm here, and I hope I can stay. 86
I'm clean and I'm neat—please don't send me 95
away!" Sue's big blue eyes twinkled. 101

How can you disappoint a dinosaur? Sue 108
stayed. I'm the only kid in the neighborhood 116
with a dinosaur for a best friend. We laugh, 125
play games, and go exploring together. We're 132
never plain. We're never ordinary. Every day is 140
an adventure! 142

---

Why did the girl let Sue stay? Why is every day an *adventure*?

# UNIT 11
# Dog Detective

# Sue Goes Missing

*by Marilyn Sprick*
*illustrated by Janet Pederson*

Look at the picture on page 54. This shows the real Sir Winston. Now look at Janet Pederson's illustration of Sir Winston on page 55. How does the illustration look like the real Sir Winston?

## Chapters 1, 2

# Vocabulary

## ★ fran·tic

**Frantic** means wildly upset because of worry or fear.

Where is he?

The boy was *frantic* when his dog ran away. If you were frantic, describe how you would feel and act.

## ★ un·dis·turbed

If something is just the way you left it, it is **undisturbed**.

When I returned, my jigsaw puzzle was *undisturbed*. What's another way to say "No one touched the puzzle"? Start with "The puzzle was . . . "

## ★ spe·cial·ty

A **specialty** is something that a person is very good at.

My mother is an artist. Her *specialty* is painting.

Dr. Seuss was an author. He wrote rhyming books. What was his specialty?

### Idioms and Expressions

## ★ come un·glued

When a person **comes unglued**, he or she is frantic and often acts a little crazy.

When Roberto lost his bus money and couldn't get home, he stomped his feet and yelled at the bus stop sign. Use our new expression to tell what happened to Roberto.

★ = New

## Chapter 1

# An Ordinary Day

It was an ordinary Friday. Nothing much was happening. I had just finished a dusty job out of town. I'd found a colony of ants. Now I was back in the office. Tick, tick, tick . . . time was not flying by.

I wrote my brother an e-mail. I opened a bag of Hound Dog Snacks. Then I settled down to read the *Chicago Times*. Suddenly, the door burst open.

A frantic, well-dressed man charged into my office. I looked up. The poor fellow clearly had a problem. A dog detective solves problems. This man had come to the right place.

I decided to wait while the man calmed down. He paced back and forth. Finally, he sat down across my desk and wiped his brow.

---

Where does this story take place? At the beginning of the chapter, what kind of day was it? What happened to change the mood of the story?

I gave the man a glass of water. Then I said, "If you have a problem, you've come to the right place. I'm Sir Winston, master detective. I leave no stone unturned. There is no problem too big or small for a dog detective to solve."

This seemed to make a difference. The man began to relax. "My name is Ross," he said. "I run the museum. I'm sure you've heard what happened." Then he sadly shook his head.

Having been out of town, I hadn't heard. So I said, "Please start from the beginning."

Director Ross began, "It was an ordinary day, just another Friday. As is my habit, I'd gone to the museum early. I put on the coffee, but something didn't seem right. I had a feeling that something was wrong. So I decided to take a walk through the museum.

"I walked through the museum. The gems were undisturbed, and the mummies were fine. So I thought to myself, 'It's just your imagination.'

---

Sir Winston is a master detective who leaves no stone unturned. What does this mean?

"But then, on my way back to the coffee pot, I crossed through the Hall of Dinosaurs. Never in a million years did I dream this could happen."

What do you think is Director Ross's problem?

**MAIN CHARACTERS**

**1.** Who are the two main characters?

**CHARACTERIZATION**

**2.** Describe Sir Winston in this story.

**CHARACTERIZATION**

**3.** Describe Director Ross.

## Chapter 2

# Unglued

It had been a quiet Friday afternoon when a frantic man had burst into my office. He was the director of the museum. I was listening to his story, but I still hadn't figured out what his problem was. So I said, "Director Ross, there's no problem too big or small that I can't solve. What's your problem?"

He looked at me. Then he said, "It's Sue. Sue is missing!"

I said, "My specialty is finding missing people. I, Sir Winston, will find your friend Sue."

The director said, "You don't understand. It's Sue. She's HUGE!"

I said carefully, "I see. Your missing friend is a large person."

The director looked at me. "No, she is HUGE. She is enormous. She is a giant."

---

What is the director's problem? What do you know about Sue? Try to imagine what Sue looks like.

Hearing the panic rise in the director's voice, I said calmly, "I see. My first clue—the missing person is a very large woman, a very, very large woman."

The director looked at me, and then he laughed. I thought to myself, "He's coming unglued. I'd better get this Sue back fast." I pulled out my notepad. A detective always asks questions and takes notes. I asked, "Color of hair?"

What does Sir Winston know about Sue? Why does Sir Winston think Director Ross is *coming unglued*? What does that mean?

The director replied, "Hair? She has no hair."

So I wrote "bald." I thought to myself, "Very, very large, bald woman. This shouldn't be too hard."

"Any scars? Tattoos? Birthmarks?"

The director thought for a moment and said, "Big teeth, she has big teeth." I nodded and wrote "big teeth."

Sir Winston has three clues. Look at the pictures. What does Sir Winston know about Sue?

## Chapter 3

# Can You Help or Not?

It had taken awhile, but I had three clues about the missing Sue. She was very, very large. She was bald, and she had big teeth. It felt like I was still missing information, so I asked, "Age?"

Director Ross rubbed his head and said, "Oh, she's ancient."

I looked at him and thought, "Strange answer." I asked, "Could you be more specific?"

The director said, "She's millions and millions of years old."

Next to age, I wrote "very old." Then I scratched it out and wrote "ancient." I asked, "Okay, now. How tall is this Sue?"

---

How is Sir Winston learning about Sue? What does Sir Winston think Sue is? What has he learned so far?

The director responded, "Just her head is five feet tall."

By now I was thinking, "This guy is really wacko." So I said, "Ross, I'm not so sure I can help you. This Sue . . . maybe she's just gone on a little vacation."

Ross looked at me. "Really," I said. "Maybe if you wait a day, she'll come back."

At that, Ross got upset again. "What?" he stormed. "You said you could solve any problem, big or small!"

Just then the door burst open again. Reporters from the *Chicago Times* were all over the place. Lights flashed. Cameras rolled, and a microphone was shoved in front of me.

**Think** **and Talk**

CHARACTERIZATION

1. What does Sir Winston know about the missing Sue?

INFERENCE

2. Why did Director Ross get angry at the end of the chapter?

EVENT

3. What happened in the last paragraph of the chapter?

CAUSE AND EFFECT

4. Why was there such a commotion?

**Chapter 4**

# No Case Too Big

Reporters from the *Chicago Times* and all the TV stations swarmed through my little office. A reporter shoved a mike in front of me and said, "Sir Winston, we hear you've taken the case of the missing dinosaur."

Dinosaur? Then it came to me. Bald, ancient, huge . . . The director was talking about a dinosaur—a T. rex, to be exact. It wasn't a missing person.

The reporters were waiting. I cleared my throat. Then I said in my deepest, most serious detective voice, "Of course. I, Sir Winston, master detective, have agreed to take the case of the missing dinosaur. No case is too big for this doggie detective. I will put my nose to the ground. I will leave no stone unturned. I, Sir Winston, will find the missing Sue."

Why do you think Sir Winston took the case of the missing Sue? What did Sir Winston mean when he said he would leave no stone unturned?

There it was. I had agreed to take the case. Director Ross smiled. We put our arms around each other's shoulders. Flashes went off. The photographers took dozens of pictures. We smiled until our faces hurt!

Finally, the commotion died down. The reporters left. Director Ross shook my paw again, thanked me, and then went back to the museum.

I reviewed my notes. Bald dinosaur, big teeth, ancient . . . Then sweat broke out across my brow. I wondered if I could solve this case. It was the biggest case I'd ever had. I started to get nervous, but then I could hear Dad saying, "Son, you can do it. You can do it."

With that, I thought, "There is no problem too big or small that this dog detective can't solve. I can do it. I can!"

Why did Sir Winston start to get nervous? Do you think Sir Winston can solve the case?

## Chapter 5

# Kidnapped

The next morning, bright and early, I went to the museum. Director Ross let me in. The coffee was perking. We sat. Director Ross talked, and I listened. A dog detective always listens. I took more notes. A dog detective always takes notes.

| CLUES | |
|---|---|
| Scientific name: | *Tyrannosaurus rex* |
| Nickname: | Sue |
| Age: | 67 million years old |
| Home: | North America |
| Found: | August 12, 1990 |
| Length: | 42 feet long |
| Height at hips: | 13 feet |
| Estimated weight: | 7 tons |
| Weight of skull: | 600 pounds |
| Length of skull: | 5 feet |
| Size of brain: | Just big enough to hold a quart of milk |
| Size of teeth: | 5 to 12 inches long |

I looked at my clues and thought, "How hard can this be? Very large dinosaur, 67 million years old, longer than a school bus, big head, small brain—not very smart, probably hungry!"

Then I put my nose to the ground. I lifted one paw. My tail shot out straight. Sue's scent was clear. I followed my nose to the door. She had left through the door. "Kidnapped!" I thought. "The dino must have been kidnapped!"

That night Director Ross went on TV. He pleaded for information about the missing dinosaur. Children all over the city were distressed. They wrote letters asking the kidnappers to return Sue.

What does this dog detective do to solve a case? What has Sir Winston learned about Sue?

**EXPLANATION**

1. What did Sir Winston think had happened to Sue?

**INFERENCE**

2. What do you think happened to Sue?

**INFERENCE**

3. Why were the children in the city distressed?

**EVENT**

4. What did the children do?

## Chapter 6

# Footprints

While the children wrote letters, the police searched through the city. I, dog detective, went back to the museum. I began by following my nose. Sue's scent went right through the door. I followed my nose. She had gone through the city and into the forest.

By eight, it was dark and my nose was quite sore. That T. rex had traveled a long, long way. I built a fire and opened a can of Lazy Dog Stew. I read my notes, and I thought. A dog detective always thinks.

The next morning, I got up at dawn. The air was cool, crisp, and clean. I stretched. I had camped near a lake. In the morning light, the blue water glistened. It almost felt like I was on a vacation. Then I saw the prints—huge dino prints in the mud.

It was then that I knew. I, Sir Winston, dog detective, would find the missing Sue.

---

How did Sir Winston end up near the lake? How did Sir Winston know he would find Sue?

I cooked a good breakfast. A dog detective always eats breakfast. Then I packed up my things and carefully put out the fire.

Before leaving the lake, I measured the prints and wrote in my notepad "large dino prints near lake." I was ready to leave, but I thought, "I'm missing something. There's another clue here. What is it?" Then I knew! The only footprints by the lake belonged to the dino. I said to myself, "Well, I'll be. I wonder why."

Why do you think Sir Winston said, "Well, I'll be"? What did Sir Winston figure out? What do you think Sir Winston wondered?

## Chapter 7

# Tracking Sue

I followed Sue's trail through the forest and mountains, then through cities and small towns. A dog detective never gives up. I knew I would find her. It was just a matter of time.

Days later, in a small place named Cozy Town, I spotted her. She wasn't easy to miss. She was playing in the park with a dozen kids at her feet. A young girl sat on Sue's head. I watched from a distance. Sue's big teeth glistened in the sun.

Sue looked happy. Since that day at the lake, I'd known. The only tracks I'd found were Sue's. There weren't any kidnappers. Sue had left on her own.

Where did Sir Winston find Sue? Who was she with? How do you think Sue got to Cozy Town?

I strolled over to Sue. She looked at me with surprisingly blue eyes. Then she roared, "How do you do? My name is Sue."

I grinned back. "Fine thanks," I barked. "My name is Sir Winston. Director Ross sent me. He's ever so worried. Where have you been?"

Sue giggled and said, "I've been on an adventure—I have! I was bored at the museum, so one night I just walked out the door. I roamed through forests, mountains, cities, and towns. Then I found a nice house and a new best friend." Sue's big blue eyes twinkled.

I saw that the dino was happy and not about to return to the museum. Now what to do? I scratched my head.

You may wonder how this all turned out. I called Director Ross and he came to Cozy Town. He came loaded with letters from kids all over the country begging for Sue's return. Sue was flattered. She was touched. She was happy to be loved.

---

Why did Sue leave the museum? What made her feel flattered, happy, and loved? What do you think will happen next?

Ross and Sue talked and talked. Finally, Sue agreed to go back to the museum, and Director Ross promised her time off. Sue would get two days off each week and two weeks off each year.

Ross, Sue, and I went back to the city. A big commotion followed—lights, cameras, celebrations! Case closed!

**Afterword:** Now two days a week and two weeks each year, in the dark of night, Sue walks out the museum door. She returns to Cozy Town where she laughs, plays games, and goes exploring with her new best friend.

CONCLUSION

**1.** What happened at the end?

SOLUTION

**2.** How was the director's problem solved?

GENRE

**3.** What makes this an imaginative story? Use examples.

INFERENCE

**4.** Why do you think this is one of the author's favorite stories?

PERSONAL RESPONSE

**5.** Did you like this story? Why or why not?

# Fluency

WEATHER
High Humity with rain
showers expected.

**Chicago Times** FINAL

# DOG DETECTIVE SUCCEEDS

from the *Chicago Times*
by reporter Bea Gull

After weeks on 3
the trail of the missing 8
dinosaur, Sir Winston, 11
master detective, and 14
Ross, museum director, 17
returned to the city with 22
Sue. The T. rex is now safely standing in 31
the Hall of Dinosaurs. She appears to 38
have been unharmed. 41

When asked about the mystery, Sir 47
Winston said, "It was a long and difficult 55
case, but I knew all along that I would 64
find Sue. A dog detective uses his nose. 72
There is no problem too big or small for a 82
dog detective!" 84

At the museum, Director Ross was quick 7
to say, "Sir Winston is a great detective, 15
perhaps the greatest detective of all time." 22

Director Ross also stated, "The 27
truckloads of letters from kids across the 34
country were important in getting Sue back. 41
Without the letters of support and everyone's 48
love, we may not have gotten Sue back." 56

# Fluency

The Hall of Dinosaurs is now back open— 8
five days per week, Saturday, Sunday, 14
Monday, Tuesday, and Wednesday. The 19
exhibit will be closed every Thursday and 26
Friday and the first week in August and 34
December. 35

When asked why the Hall would be 42
closed, Director Ross simply said, "It's in the 50
best interest of Sue and the museum. Our 58
other wonderful exhibits—the mummies, 63
gems, space, and so on—will remain open 71
seven days a week." 75

When asked where Sue had been and 82
what happened to the kidnappers, Director 88
Ross and Sir Winston had no answer. Some 96
people say that Sue was unhappy and left, 104
but we do not know for sure. 111

Who solved the case of the missing dinosaur? Why is the dino exhibit closed two days each week and two weeks each year? Why won't Sir Winston and Director Ross explain why Sue was missing?

# Fluency

## Sue: The Real Story
*by Paula Rich*

One hot day in the summer of 1990, a 9
woman named Sue was on a fossil-hunting 17
expedition in South Dakota. Her truck had a 25
flat tire. While the other fossil hunters were 33
fixing the tire, Sue wandered over to some rocky 42
cliffs. She looked up and saw giant dinosaur 50
bones sticking out of the cliff. They were the 59
remains of a Tyrannosaurus rex! The dinosaur 66
fossil was named Sue after the woman who 74
discovered it. 76

The bones were removed from the rock 83
with great care. Scientists soon realized that 90
Sue was the largest, most complete T. rex ever 99
discovered. More than 200 bones were located. 106

Now the enormous skeleton of Sue stands 113
in the Field Museum in Chicago. Scientists have 121
done a lot of research on Sue's bones to find out 132
how she lived. 135

What did this real Sue discover? Why was the T. rex named Sue?

Scientists have learned that the part of Sue's <sup>8</sup> brain used for smell was huge, so we know that <sup>18</sup> the sense of smell was probably very important <sup>26</sup> to a T. rex. Sue's teeth were very large, strong, <sup>36</sup> and sharp, so scientists think Sue was probably <sup>44</sup> a meat eater. <sup>47</sup>

One thing we can't tell from the fossil is <sup>56</sup> whether Sue was male or female. Even though <sup>64</sup> Sue now has a woman's name, we don't know if <sup>74</sup> she really was a she! <sup>79</sup>

What did the scientists learn from the bones?

# Glossary

## bicker

**Bicker** means to argue about things that are not important.

Sammy and Will *bickered* about who should be first in line.

## boast

**Boast** means to brag. When someone boasts, he or she talks proudly about something.

Courtney *boasted* about winning first place.

## crouch

**Crouch** means to squat down close to the ground.

The children *crouched* in the sand.

## curious

Someone who is **curious** wants to know more about something.

Sandy was very *curious* about plants and wanted to learn more.

## definitely

**Definitely** means for sure.

If you drop an egg, it will *definitely* make a mess.

## determined

When you try very hard and do not give up, you are **determined**.

Stan was *determined* to win the race.

## dinosaur

A **dinosaur** is an extinct animal that roamed Earth millions of years ago. The word "dinosaur" means terrible lizard.

*Dinosaurs* walked around Earth for millions of years.

## expedition

An **expedition** is a special journey to study or discover something.

The astronauts went on an *expedition* to the moon.

## extinct

**Extinct** means died out. Animals and plants that are extinct are no longer found on Earth.

Dinosaurs are *extinct*.

## fascinate

**Fascinate** means to hold someone's interest. Things that fascinate us are very interesting.

Insects *fascinate* Ann, so she wants to study them.

# Glossary

## fossil

A **fossil** is the remains of a plant or animal that lived long ago. A fossil is made of rock or found in rock.

My friend found a fish *fossil* near the river.

## frantic

**Frantic** means wildly upset because of worry or fear.

The boy was *frantic* when his dog disappeared.

Where is he?

## hesitate

**Hesitate** means to stop before saying or doing something. You hesitate because you aren't sure what to do.

The water in the pool was cold, so I *hesitated* before jumping in.

## imagine

**Imagine** means to make a picture of something in your mind. You can also imagine how something might smell, taste, and feel.

*Imagine* life without cars.

## insist

**Insist** means to communicate very strongly what you want or how you feel.

Mom *insisted* that I clean my room.

## locate

**Locate** means to find where something is.

We used the map to *locate* the treasure.

## obsessed

To be **obsessed** with something means to think about that thing all the time.

The boy was *obsessed* with his toy car.

## organize

**Organize** means to arrange or plan things.

Louisa *organized* the fruit on the table.

## realize

**Realize** means to suddenly understand something.

Tom *realized* he was late for dinner.

## remains

**Remains** are what is left of something.

Dinosaur *remains* include teeth, bones, eggs, and tracks.

# Glossary

### roam

**Roam** means to wander or walk around freely.

Long ago, dinosaurs *roamed* the Earth.

### specialty

A **specialty** is something that a person is very good at.

My mother is an artist. Her *specialty* is painting.

### undisturbed

If something is just the way you left it, it is **undisturbed**.

When I returned, my jigsaw puzzle was *undisturbed*.

### vast

A place that is **vast** is very great in size. It is enormous.

Space is *vast*.

### weary

**Weary** means very tired.

Sally was *weary* from her long hike.

## come unglued

When a person **comes unglued**, he or she is frantic and often acts a little crazy.

Roberto *came unglued* when he realized he'd forgotten his bus money.

## save the day

**Save the day** means to keep something from going wrong.

We thought we were lost, but Mike had a map and *saved the day.*